D1411632

WHAT IT MEANS TO BE
SERIES

PUBLISHER	Joseph R. DeVarennes
PUBLICATION DIRECTOR	Kenneth H. Pearson
ADVISORS	Roger Aubin
	Robert Furlonger
EDITORIAL MANAGER	Jocelyn Smyth
EDITORS	Ann Martin
	Shelley McGuinness
	Robin Rivers
	Mayta Tannenbaum
ARTISTS	Richard Comely
	Greg Elliott
	Summer Morse
	Barbara Pileggi
	Steve Pileggi
	Mike Stearns
PRODUCTION MANAGER	Ernest Homewood
PRODUCTION ASSISTANTS	Catherine Gordon
	Kathy Kishimoto
PUBLICATION ADMINISTRATOR	Anna Good

Canadian Cataloguing in Publication Data

Elliot, Jacqueline
  What it means to be—confident

(What it means to be; 24)
ISBN 0-7172-2242-X

1. Self-confidence — Juvenile literature.
I. Pileggi, Steve.   II. Title.   III. Title: Confident.   IV. Series.

BJ1533.S27E44   1987   j179'.9   C87-095067-3

Copyright © 1987 by Grolier Limited. All rights reserved.

Sidalmir Regular 1991-92 Grolier $7.10

WHAT IT MEANS TO BE...

CONFIDENT

Written by
Jacqueline Elliot

Illustrated by
Richard Comely

Confident people believe in themselves.

"I've got an idea for theme week at school," said Ryan as he walked to school with Kim.

"Doesn't Ms. Barclay decide that?" asked Kim.

"I'm sure she wouldn't mind a suggestion," he explained. "I think we should be pioneers."

Kim wrinkled her nose, but Ryan continued. "We could dress up in old-fashioned clothes and make food and do crafts just like people used to do a long time ago."

"I don't know . . . it sounds kind of boring."

"No, Kim, it would be fun," Ryan said excitedly. "And we could sing old songs."

"Hmmm." Kim still wasn't convinced.

As soon as school started, Ryan put up his hand. He explained his idea to the teacher and how much fun he thought they could have being pioneers.

Ms. Barclay smiled. "You make it sound exciting, Ryan. I think we should do it." Everyone in the class agreed. Even Kim was beginning to think she wouldn't mind being a pioneer after all.

You must believe in yourself in order to carry out your ideas.

A confident person enjoys trying new things.

Hannah was eating her cereal one morning. She was feeling a little nervous. Today was the day a new teacher was coming to give a French lesson.

Her mother sat down beside her. "Are you looking forward to learning French?"

"No," Hannah replied. "I'm scared. I think it's going to be hard."

"Oh, I wouldn't worry," her mother encouraged her. "You like new things and you learn quickly. I'm sure you'll do fine."

"Do you really think so?" Hannah asked anxiously.

"Of course," her mother said as she squeezed Hannah's shoulder. "I bet you'll even have fun."

Hannah ran all the way home from school. She could hardly wait to tell her mother about her French class. "I'm home, Mom," she called. "Where are you?"

"I'm in the kitchen," her mother answered.

"Oh, Mom, the new French teacher is really nice. She taught us how to say hello and goodbye in French."

"Did you enjoy yourself?"

"Yes, and tomorrow she's going to teach us a French song," Hannah exclaimed.

"That sounds wonderful. So you're not nervous about learning French anymore?"

"No, it *is* fun," she answered. "Do you want to hear me say hello?"

"Sure," said her mother.

"*Bonjour, bonjour,*" said Hannah giggling.

If you're confident, you look forward to new experiences.

It takes time to build confidence.

Colette was sitting on the front steps watching her friends ride by on their bicycles. She had fallen off her bike the day before and scraped her arm. She felt scared of bike riding. Her dad came out and sat down beside her. Colette gave a big sigh.

Her dad looked at her and raised his eyebrows. "Why aren't you riding around with your friends?"

"I don't feel like it," replied Colette.

"How's your arm?"

"It's okay," she said.

"Are you nervous about getting back on your bike?" he asked.

"Well, uh, maybe a little."

Her father took her hand. "That's okay. It's natural to feel a bit frightened."

"It is?"

He nodded his head. "You had a scare when you fell off. It will take a while to feel comfortable again on your bike." Then he smiled. "Do you remember how long it took you to learn to ride your two-wheeler?"

Colette looked thoughtful. "I guess it took a while."

"A while?!" her father said, laughing. "I remember spending a whole summer running along beside your bike."

"Oh, yeah," she replied.

"Then, when I took off your training wheels, you went too fast and crashed into the bushes at the end of the block."

"I thought I'd never learn," said Colette.

"But little by little you got better and better," he remarked. "Soon you were very sure of yourself."

She chuckled. "That was fun. I guess I could get on my bike and give it a try."

"Sounds like a good idea," her father said. "Do you want me to run along beside you?"

"No thanks, Dad." She gave him a big hug. "I think I'll be fine."

Becoming confident about your skills takes time. Sometimes things go wrong and you may feel less sure of yourself. It's important to be patient as you rebuild your confidence.

Confident people enjoy their friends' successes.

Miss Foster told the kindergarten class first thing in the morning that she had a special announcement.

"The grade ones are going to be doing the play *Jack and the Beanstalk*. Our class is going to make the beanstalk."

"Won't it be hard to make?" asked Janice. "It will take us forever. I think they should get an older class to make it."

"I think it sounds terrific," said Mitchell.

"We can work on it together. It will be the best beanstalk ever," predicted Hannah.

The next morning, there were two small ladders and a big box at the back of the classroom.

"This is the start of our beanstalk," Miss Foster explained. "Can you guess what we're going to do next?"

"I know!" cried Tammy. "We're going to cover it with paper leaves."

"And paint it green and brown," added Mitchell.

"It will never work," whispered Janice. "We're too little."

"Now you all have to help each other," said Miss Foster. "Remember each of you has strong points and weak ones. Ask for help when you need it."

Mitchell said, "Janice, I can show you how to draw the leaves if you can help me put them together. I'm not very good at gluing things."

"I think it's hopeless," moaned Janice.

Mitchell brought out the book *Jack and the Beanstalk*. He studied the pictures of the leaves and traced out the shapes. Then Janice cut them out.

"This is fun," laughed Mitchell.

Hubbard Elem. School Library
Culloden Road
Forsyth, GA 31029

Janice tried to draw a leaf. "This isn't any good. My leaf didn't come out evenly."

"It takes practice," he said. "Keep trying."

After several more attempts Janice finally drew a well-shaped leaf. Then she drew another and another. She started to enjoy herself.

"They look great," said Mitchell. "They're even better than mine."

Miss Foster came over to see how they were doing. "Excellent work, Janice. Can I use your leaves as examples for the rest of the class?"

"Sure." Janice beamed.

"Now you can show me how to paste the leaves on," said Mitchell.

"You bet," grinned Janice. "You know, I think this beanstalk is going to look really good."

When your friends do well at something—especially a new task—you should be happy for them and offer praise.

It's not good to be over-confident.

Dylan and Joey were sitting on Dylan's front porch talking. Paul zoomed past on his skateboard.

"Wow," said Joey. "Paul's so fast. I wish I could skateboard like him."

"Paul has been practicing for a long time," Dylan explained. "That's why he makes it look easy."

When Paul came by again, Joey called, "Hey, Paul, you're really good. Can you do the trick that the older kids do where you spin around on your back wheels three or four times?"

"Sure I can," boasted Paul. He was pleased with Joey's compliment, and he wanted to impress Dylan too.

Paul hopped onto his skateboard and sped down the block. Then he turned around and headed back toward Dylan's house. He wanted to try the trick right in front of his audience. Paul tilted the skateboard up and tried to spin around just like he'd seen some other kids do. But he hadn't practiced this move before. Suddenly he flew right off the skateboard. Fortunately he landed on the grass.

Joey and Dylan ran over to him. "Are you okay?" asked Dylan, bending over Paul.

"Did you hurt yourself?" asked Joey.

"I'm all right," replied Paul. He brushed himself off and got up. His knee hurt a bit. More than anything his pride was hurt.

Confidence cannot take the place of effort and practice. It's important to believe in your ability to learn something—but then you still have to *learn* it.

You can gain confidence by challenging yourself.

Eva, Kim and Colette went to the public library. Once they got there, Kim gathered a pile of books and took them to a table.

"I think you might like this one," she said to Eva.

"I love fairy tales," exclaimed Eva. "But this book looks too difficult for me to read."

Colette picked it up and flipped through the pages. "The words are too big and there aren't any pictures. Let's put it back."

Eva looked at it again. "No, I think I'd like to try reading it. I want to become a better reader. This is a way for me to start. And I can always get my parents to help me if I get stuck."

Once you learn how to do something, you can improve your skills by trying a more difficult level. It is especially important to become a confident reader.

A confident person gives credit where it is due.

"Cameron," called Ryan, "can you help me?"

Cameron went over to the kitchen table where his brother was working. "What are you doing?"

"I'm trying to get this puzzle finished, but I'm stuck. I can't find the right pieces."

Cameron picked up a blue piece. "Well, this looks like it should go here." It fit perfectly. "And this looks like it fits over there."

"You make it look easy!" exclaimed Ryan.

"Forget about the colors for a minute," explained Cameron. "Try to find the right shape."

Ryan tried to find puzzle pieces the way his brother had shown him. Cameron helped too. By the time their mother got home they had finished the puzzle.

"You sure did that fast, Ryan," she said.

"Cameron's been helping me," explained Ryan. "I couldn't have done it without him."

Asking for help from others doesn't mean you aren't confident. It shows that you are trying hard and are willing to learn from others. Remember to recognize their help.

Confident people are willing to stand alone.

Joey and Jason saw Dylan hurrying along the street in a red checked shirt, a bolo tie and blue slacks. They looked at each other and started chuckling.

Joey gave a big wolf whistle. "Where are you going, handsome?"

Dylan blushed. "I'm going to see my grandmother."

"Why are you all dressed up?" asked Jason.

"Uh, well, I'm helping her," explained Dylan.

"Oh really?" said Joey. "What are you helping her do?"

"Square dance," Dylan mumbled.

"What?!" laughed Jason.

"I'm her partner for square dancing," Dylan explained and walked away quickly.

When Dylan and his grandmother took a break from square dancing and were sipping lemonade, he told her what had happened.

"I was so embarrassed," he said. "Nobody else does square dancing."

"But you like it, don't you?" his grandmother asked.

"Oh yes. It's great."

She smiled. "And you like the clothes?"

"I feel like a real cowboy," he replied.

"So what are you going to tell your friends the next time you see them?" his grandmother asked.

Dylan looked puzzled for a moment and then he said, "I'll tell them all about square dancing and invite them to come."

She patted his shoulder. "Ready for another dance?"

"Okay!"

Sometimes your friends may tease you for doing things they don't do. If you do what you enjoy without worrying about being laughed at, it shows that you are confident.

Some people are naturally more confident than others.

Jason and Bobby were walking home from school one afternoon.

"Are you excited about being the giant in *Jack and the Beanstalk?*" asked Bobby.

"Yeah, I can't wait," said Jason. "I'm practicing my lines every night. I love being in plays."

"I only have a few lines to remember," said Bobby nervously, "but I keep forgetting them. I wish I wasn't in the play at all."

"Well, why don't you come over to my house and I can help you?" suggested Jason. "Once you learn your lines, you'll feel a lot better."

After supper Bobby went to Jason's house. At first he listened while Jason recited his lines. Jason already knew most of them by heart.

"Okay, Bobby," said Jason. "It's your turn. Go ahead."

But Bobby only managed to say a few words before he stopped. "I can't go on. I get too nervous."

"Come on, Bobby, you can do it. First try reading the lines from your script. Don't worry about me listening to you. Just concentrate on how you sound. Then you can work on memorizing them."

Bobby read the lines aloud a few times. Then he tried them without looking at his script.
After a few attempts Bobby got them right.

"That's great!" cried Jason. "You've got it."

Sometimes your friends may lack confidence. You can help them by being encouraging.

Confident people can take criticism.

Tammy and Janice were doing somersaults in Janice's backyard. "I'm going to be an Olympic gymnast when I grow up," announced Janice.

"Wow!" exclaimed Tammy. "That would be great. Maybe I will be a gymnast too."

"If you practice, I bet you could," answered Janice. "Let's do some cartwheels."

As Janice watched her friend, she noticed that Tammy wasn't landing right. "You do somersaults really well," she said. "But your cartwheels are a little crooked."

"What do you mean?" asked Tammy, looking surprised.

"Here, I'll show you." Janice did a cartwheel.

"Oh . . ." Tammy felt strange because Janice had criticized her but she did want to learn how to do cartwheels right. "I'll try again."

Soon Tammy's cartwheels were as good as Janice's.

Everyone has strengths and weaknesses. Do not be upset if someone gives you some helpful criticism. Listen to the advice and try to improve.

Confident people are good losers.

Eva was sitting on a swing at the park staring at her feet. She felt miserable. She didn't want to do anything or even see anyone. Just then Colette walked over and sat down.

"Hi," she said. She started pumping her legs and soon she was zooming through the air. "Let's see who can go the highest," called Colette.

"No," mumbled Eva.

Colette slowed down. "Is something wrong?"

"I wanted our team to win the ball hockey game and we lost. We were terrible."

"Well, maybe next time we'll do better," suggested Colette.

"But I wanted to win," complained Eva. She turned to Colette. "Why aren't you upset?"

"I love playing hockey," said Colette. "I don't mind winning or losing. Anyway, we can practice hard and we'll do better in our next game."

"Do you think so?" asked Eva, looking hopeful.

"Sure," answered Colette.

If you're confident, you don't let losing upset you. You know the important thing is how hard you try.

Having confidence makes things happen.

Finally the night of the school play arrived. Children and parents crowded into the gym to watch *Jack and the Beanstalk*. Everyone thought Jason was wonderful as the giant. They laughed and cheered. Bobby came on stage and said his small part. He pronounced everything clearly and didn't forget a single word.

When the play was finished Bobby's parents gave him a big hug.

"You were wonderful," beamed his dad.

"That was a fine play," said his mother. "Your lines were perfect."

"Thanks for having confidence in me," said Bobby. "I sure didn't have much in myself."

When Bobby saw Jason he ran over to him and said, "Thanks a lot."

"Hey, that's okay. Do you want to be in the school play next year?" asked Jason.

"I sure do," replied Bobby. "Maybe I can even get to say more lines."

When everyone had cleared away from the stage the kindergarten class went up and showed their parents the beanstalk.

"It took us two weeks to make this," Miss Foster explained. "The whole class worked together and did a wonderful job."

All of the children gathered around and talked about how much fun the play had been.

"Let's make something else for next year's play," said Tammy.

"Yes," agreed Mitchell.

"I can hardly wait," said Janice.

Confident people believe in themselves and are always willing to encourage others. They work hard and enjoy their own and their friends' successes. Here are some ways to be confident:

- Look forward to new experiences.
- Accept helpful criticism.
- Ask for help when you need it.
- Remember that it takes time and practice to learn something.

Printed and bound in U.S.A.